Published by The Omnibus Publishing™
www.omnibuspub.com

Special thanks to Parent Pages contributor & Acquistions Editor,
Children's Division, Jamie Roeder, MS

The Omnibus Publishing™
info@omnibuspub.com

Or write to:
The Omnibus Publishing™
Attn: Permissions Department
5422 Ebenezer Rd.
POB 152
Baltimore, MD 21128

ISBN 978-0-9960458-5-8

© 2015 The Omnibus Publishing™, a part of Reading Pandas, Inc.
Baltimore - MD - USA

Printed in the United States of America - USA. 1st printing. 05/2015

THIS BOOK BELONGS TO

ST. James Pre-School,
Explore the world
one book at a time!
Best Wishes,
Krissy M. atchisor

This book is dedicated to my husband, Patrick, and daughters, Penelope, Julia, and Alexandra.

I would also like to acknowledge my brother, Leon, whose passion for surfing and traveling are the inspiration behind this series.

-KMA

LEE LEE
THE SURFING MONKEY
HANGS TEN

BY KRISSY MACH-ATCHISON

ILLUSTRATIONS BY MICHAELA SCHUETT

Lee Lee is a monkey who loves to SURF!
But he likes the waves found on his home turf.

One day he decides he must go explore the many oceans beyond his front door.

"Where should I go?"
He cannot decide.

"I've got it!" he says, as his eyes open wide!

The "Land Down Under" is first on his list, to find out new things he does not know exist.

After a super long flight, he finally arrives,

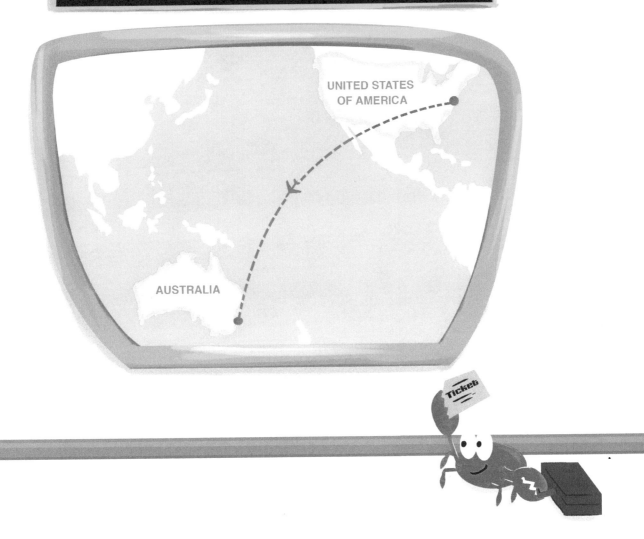

with a kangaroo, koala, and emu by his side.

He goes to the ocean with his surfboard in hand.

He kicks off his flip-flops and runs through the sand.

He paddles and hangs ten along with his friends, a little sad knowing his adventure will end.

Although it is time for Lee Lee to go home,
he knows there are many more places to roam.

They all say, "Good-bye!" as
he gets on the plane,

then a map of the world pops into his brain!

Now he sits on
the plane feeling
a little perplexed,
as he thinks
to himself ...

UNITED STATES OF AMERICA

"Where to surf next?"

PUNTARENAS

LIMON

SAN JOSE

COSTA RICA

Australian Animal Fun Facts

Koalas

- Koalas are mostly nocturnal and sleep about 18 hours a day.
- A Koala's diet consists mainly of eucalyptus leaves which makes them smell like cough drops.
- Koalas are good swimmers.
- Koalas are not bears, they are marsupials.

Emus

- Emus have three toes on each foot.
- Emus are flightless birds.
- Emus can sprint up to 30 miles per hour.
- Males grunt like pigs and females make loud booming noises.

Australian Animal Fun Facts

Kangaroos

- There are four species of kangaroos.
- An adult male kangaroo is called a Jack.
- Kangaroos cannot walk backwards.
- Kangaroos are Marsupials

PARENT PAGES

Reading together is a great way to talk and listen to your child. It is an effective way to teach your child to interact with the text in a story. This will result in strong comprehension, as well as enhanced writing and communication skills in school and at home.

Use the discussion questions below while reading this book. It will be fun to hear your child's thoughts and see their ability to make connections in every day life. Happy reading!

1. Our illustrators can be sneaky sometimes! Can you find the crab on each page?

2. Have you ever been to a beach like Lee Lee? If so, do you remember the name?

3. How do you think the water feels? Describe how you think the sand feels.

4. How do maps help people?

5. Have you ever been on an airplane? Where did you go?

6. Why do you think Lee Lee needs to ride in an airplane instead of a car to get to Australia?

7. What do you think Lee Lee packed in his suitcase?

8. Lee Lee is excited to surf with his friends. What is an activity you like to do with your friends?

9. Why is Lee Lee sad?

10. Have you ever had to say goodbye to someone and felt sad?

11. How did Lee Lee solve his problem of feeling sad? What can you do if you feel sad?

12. If you could go anywhere in the world, where would you want to go?

CPSIA information can be obtained at www.ICGtesting.com
Printed in the USA
LVOW01*0842030615

440998LV00004B/5/P